The Foragers' Workbook

TINY ORCHARD HOMESTEAD INC.

The Foragers' Workbook

Plan for Successful Wild Foraging and the
Use of Medicinal and Edible Plants

By M. Thiessen

Illustrations by Danielle Powell

Disclaimer
This workbook is meant for reader-use only and not intended to be a "how-to" guide for consuming or using wild plants. The author does not recommend experimentation while foraging and cautions that many plants, including certain traditional medicines, are poisonous and can cause harm. By reading and using this workbook, the reader acknowledges the risks of harm in foraging, and, at all times, the reader accepts all responsibility and liability for any harm that may occur while foraging or from the use or misuse of this workbook.

Dedication

My children, may you grow in understanding and wisdom as the years pass. I created this workbook for you, and I pray that it will be a useful tool for each of you.

Dani, you are immensely talented and I am so thankful for the beautiful sketches you created for this workbook.

To Shannon, and Mary, my foraging companions, you each hold a special place in my heart. I am grateful for your willingness to share wisdom and for making time to go exploring with me.

Endless thanks to my husband and all the members of my family, as well as Ashley, Krystal and the nice & supportive friends at work for listening to my dreams, and for your encouragement.

Table of Contents

Specimen Quick Reference Chart

1. _____	26. _____
2. _____	27. _____
3. _____	28. _____
4. _____	29. _____
5. _____	30. _____
6. _____	31. _____
7. _____	32. _____
8. _____	33. _____
9. _____	34. _____
10. _____	35. _____
11. _____	36. _____
12. _____	37. _____
13. _____	38. _____
14. _____	39. _____
15. _____	40. _____
16. _____	41. _____
17. _____	42. _____
18. _____	43. _____
19. _____	44. _____
20. _____	45. _____
21. _____	46. _____
22. _____	47. _____
23. _____	48. _____
24. _____	49. _____
25. _____	50. _____

My Story

Dill *(Anethum Graveolens)*

The Mystery Apple Tree

When I was a university student my friend Shannon and I set out to find apple trees to forage from. She found a beautifully heavy-laden tree and brought me there one Saturday morning. The tree was on public property and the apples were delicious. I can't exactly remember what we did with all the apples but we both had experience with making apple sauce and juice, so that was likely their fate. The next year I wanted to go back, but I couldn't remember where the tree was. I drove around several times trying to find it, but I never found it again. I have since moved several times and I doubt if I will get the opportunity to pick from it again. This was the start of my wild food journey and in a way, it was the start of The Foragers' Workbook.

I have found joy in foraging several times over in the 15 years since that apple tree held my attention. I have foraged for a variety of edible and medicinal wild plants. I found that in the upheaval of 2020 and beyond, wild food has been something that has calmed me, humbled me, and brought great satisfaction. I want my kids to know how to forage. I want them to know where to forage and what to do with their findings.

My husband's family has lived in one small farming community on the prairie for three generations. It's the type of place where you give directions by the name of the corner where someone lived 30 years ago despite there no longer being a house there. At the big rock turn left. That kind of place. My kids may be the fourth generation to choose to stay in this area. I want them to know it well, and value what it offers.

Every foraging field guide I bought told me about the plants I might see in my climate. It took me a long time however to figure out a useful format for my notes, recording what I found around me. I now have this workbook for myself. As I am gathering my harvest, I no longer wonder which cookbook and recipe I used last time. This workbook provides spots for these detailed notes.

I also look to the future and intend to leave my kids this book as a valuable keepsake that they can use. As they get older, they can start their own copies. I want them to know that there is a Saskatoon berry patch on the north side of the creek. They must call ahead to ask the farmer who owns that land for permission to go there each July, and to watch for bears, who love those berries as much as we do.

No other book they find is going to tell them about this area, about exactly where that mystery apple tree is located and what the landowner's phone number is.

I feel humbled that I can support people in their foraging journey. It is my hope that this workbook will be useful to you in the years to come. With any luck it will get dog-eared and be passed on to the ones you love. They may never *need* to know these things, but with any luck they will understand it's value and treasure the information you have thoughtfully collected.

If you need some support with getting started, you can follow me on Instagram @tinyorchardhomestead or follow the hashtag #theforagersworkbook to see me use my own copy. I am excited to document my own foraging finds and teach others along the way.

M. Thiessen

P.S. As an independent publisher, your thoughts about this workbook are meaningful to us and others who may consider purchasing this book. Please consider leaving a review, which will help others on their own foraging journey.

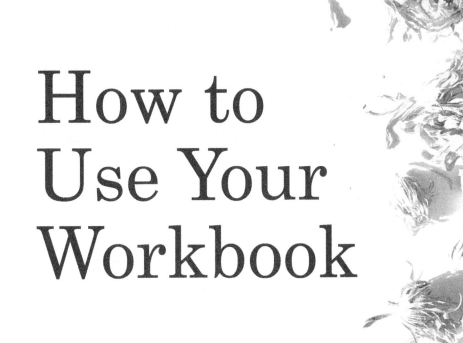

How to Use Your Workbook

Calendula (Calendula officinalis)

Specimen # _____ *Name of the item you found* _____

> *Sketch key location elements (a fence, road sign, riverbank, or treeline etc.) of where you located this item so that you can find it again in a different season or year.*

Where

Record information about location such as which street, river, whose field, and

the phone number of the land owner or municipality to ask permission to forage.

When you call, ask about any fertilizing or pesticides being used in that location.

What

What did you find? What is the scientific or Latin name?

What part of this plant are you wanting to use? (root, leaf, bark, fruit, etc.)

Only take the part of the plant you intend to use. Leave the rest intact.

Which field guides did you use for help? Note the page number.

When

When did you find it? What life cycle stage is the plant in now?

Make a note to come back to this spot during harvesting season.

Use the Harvest Reference Pages at the back of this workbook.

 Sketch

*Draw a sketch
or place a photo.*

Why

Why are you interested in harvesting this?

_____

Is any part of it edible?

_____

Can it be used medicinally?

_____

What unique properties does it have which may make it useful?

_____

_____

How

How do you harvest the part you need, safely?

_____

Which recipe book and page will you use?

_____

How did you use it? Is it going to be dried, fermented, eaten raw, boiled, etc.?

_____

_____

_____

_____

_____

_____

_____

_____

Plan
Before
You Pick

Mint (*Mentha*)

List of Edible or Medicinal Plants To Find

_____	_____
_____	_____
_____	_____
_____	_____
_____	_____
_____	_____
_____	_____
_____	_____
_____	_____
_____	_____
_____	_____
_____	_____
_____	_____
_____	_____

My Safety Tips and Warnings

There is an element of danger when foraging. Many wild edibles also have dangerous lookalikes, it is important to forage with someone who is experienced in identifying wild edibles. Wild animals, insects, allergic reactions, dehydration, and getting disoriented are among other dangers, which must be considered. If in doubt, leave it alone.

Disclaimer: These workbook pages and tips are meant for reader-use only and not intended to be a "how-to" guide for consuming wild plants. These tips are not intended to take the place of professional information concerning safe practices and dangers of foraging. Do not consume, collect or touch any plants or foods if you are in doubt to their safety!

Sustainable Practices

Less is more. Foragers usually have a set maximum for how much to harvest. The general rule is to have a good look around at what is available in an area and to not take more than 10%. If a species is at risk, take even less or none at all. Having a plan for your harvest is important so that the items you take do not go to waste. As you gather tips about sustainably foraging, keep track of them here, for quick reference.

_____

_____

_____

_____

_____

_____

_____

_____

_____

_____

_____

_____

_____

                _____

                _____

                _____

                _____

                _____

                _____

My Resources

Record which handbooks, guidebooks, recipe books, websites, research universities, names of plant experts, social media accounts, apps, wild edible identification organizations, local foraging clubs or guides that you use or hope to use.

_____

_____

_____

_____

_____

_____

_____

_____

_____

_____

_____

_____

_____

_____

_____

_____

_____

_____

_____

_____

_____

_____

Plant Anatomy

Spend some time learning about plant anatomy. Research the different types of stems, leaves, branching patterns, seeds, root systems, flowers and other essential elements of the plants you are interested in, and use this space to record important details you don't want to forget. Never experiment with plants, always make sure it is properly identified by a professional.

Fungi Structure

Spend some time learning about the anatomy of fungi if you intend to forage it. Research the types of caps, gills, and stems, and why it is important to note what the mushroom is growing on, as well as other crucial details such as what colour the gills are. Never experiment with fungi, always make sure that it is properly identified by a professional.

My Environment

Research your climate and hardiness zone to see which plants may be available to you. Record key words about your location such as Boreal Shield, or Zone 3b. You might also want to include information such as your estimated frost dates in spring and winter.

_____

_____

_____

_____

_____

_____

_____

_____

_____

_____

_____

_____

_____

_____

_____

_____

_____

_____

My Tools and Supply Checklist

Plan ahead to make sure you have what you need. Items such as a container or bag to put your harvest into, a knife or cutting tool, some gloves, a small trowel, sun protection, insect protection, water and solid footwear may be a good start to your list.

_____

_____

_____

_____

_____

_____

_____

_____

_____

_____

_____

_____

_____

_____

_____

_____

_____

_____

_____

_____

_____

Definitions

Dehydrate: *verb* to remove water from (food) in order to preserve and store it.

Flour: *noun* a powder made by grinding raw grains, roots, beans, nuts, or seeds.

Infuse: *verb* to soak (herbs, etc.) in liquid to extract the flavor or healing properties.

Poultice: *noun* a soft, moist mass of material, typically of plant material or flour, applied to the body to relieve soreness and inflammation and kept in place with a cloth.

Salve: *noun* an ointment used to promote healing of the skin or as protection.

Tea: *noun* a hot drink made by infusing the dried crushed leaves of the tea plant in boiling water.

Tincture: *noun* a concentrated liquid herbal extract made from plants and used as herbal medicine.

_____

_____

_____

_____

_____

_____

_____

_____

_____

Make a Map

Box Elder Tree (*Acer Negundo*)

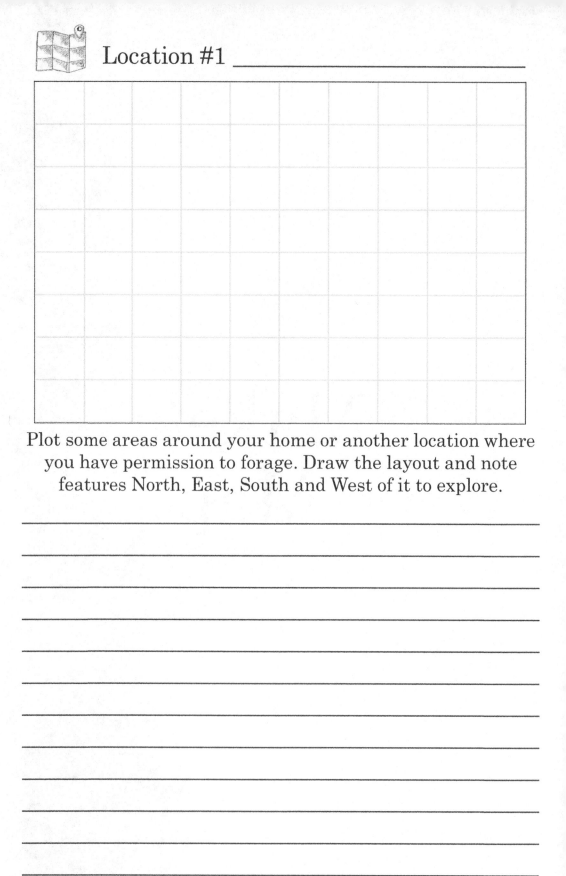

Location #1 _____

Plot some areas around your home or another location where
you have permission to forage. Draw the layout and note
features North, East, South and West of it to explore.

_____

_____

_____

_____

_____

_____

_____

_____

_____

_____

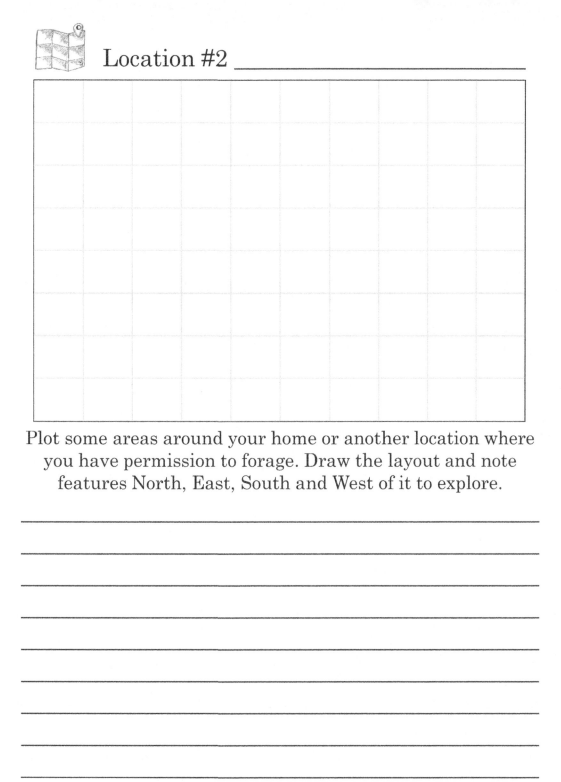

Location #2 _____

Plot some areas around your home or another location where you have permission to forage. Draw the layout and note features North, East, South and West of it to explore.

_____

_____

_____

_____

_____

_____

_____

_____

_____

_____

_____

_____

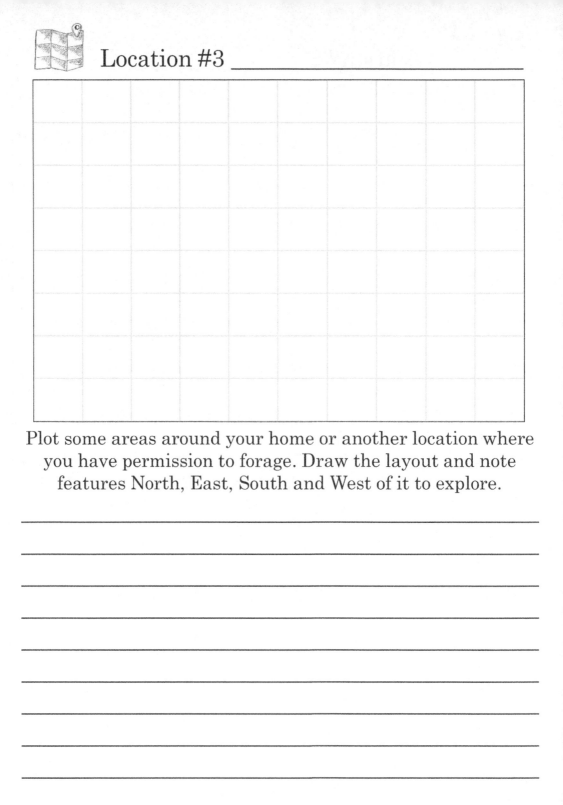

Location #3 _____

Plot some areas around your home or another location where you have permission to forage. Draw the layout and note features North, East, South and West of it to explore.

_____

_____

_____

_____

_____

_____

_____

_____

_____

_____

_____

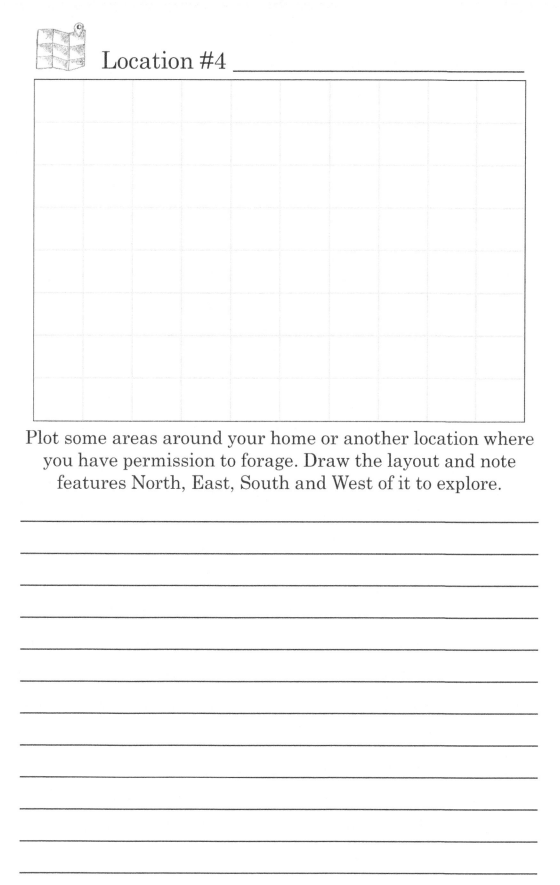

Location #4 _____

Plot some areas around your home or another location where
you have permission to forage. Draw the layout and note
features North, East, South and West of it to explore.

_____

_____

_____

_____

_____

_____

_____

_____

_____

_____

_____

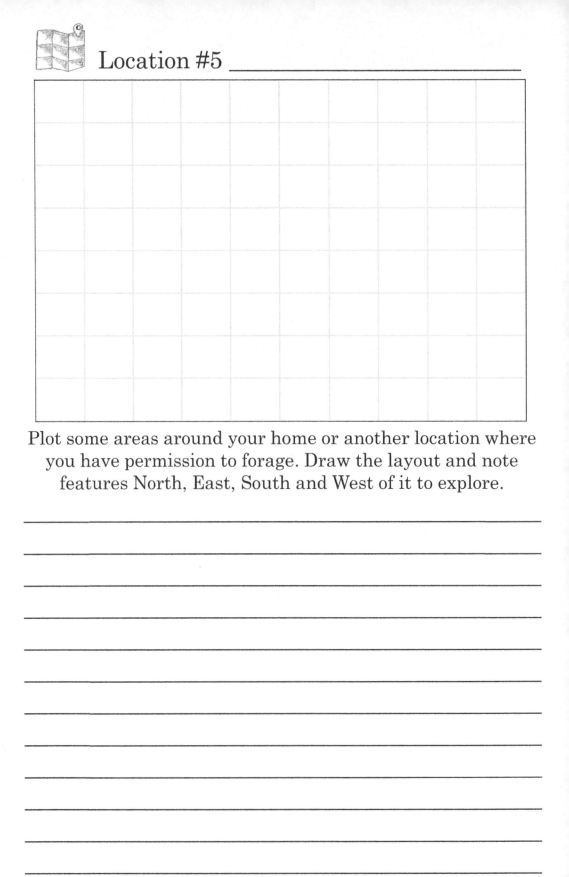

Location #5 _____

Plot some areas around your home or another location where you have permission to forage. Draw the layout and note features North, East, South and West of it to explore.

_____

_____

_____

_____

_____

_____

_____

_____

_____

_____

_____

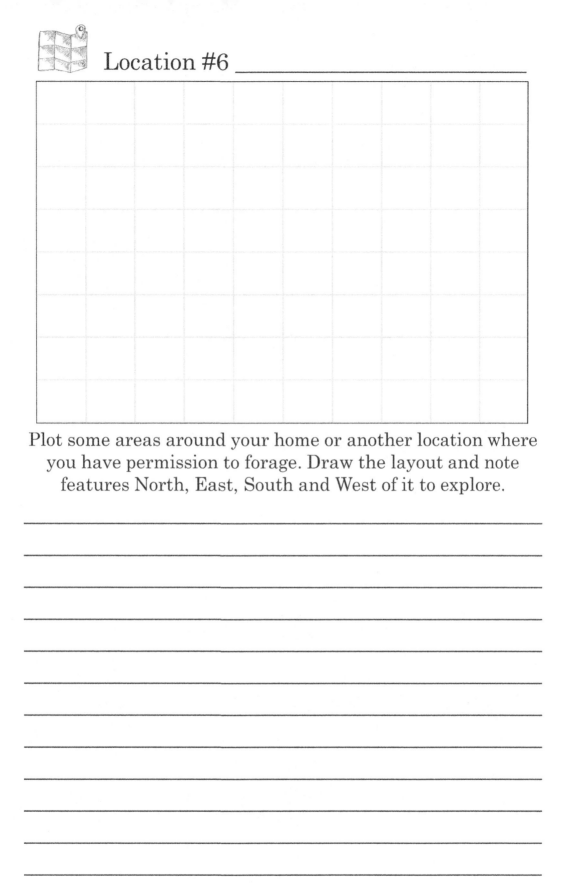

Location #6 _____

Plot some areas around your home or another location where you have permission to forage. Draw the layout and note features North, East, South and West of it to explore.

_____

_____

_____

_____

_____

_____

_____

_____

_____

_____

_____

My Foraged Finds

Rose Hips *(Rosa Acicularis)*

Specimen 1 _____

Where

What

When

Why

How

Specimen 2 _____

Where

What

When

Why

How

Specimen 3 _____

Where

What

When

Why

How

Specimen 4 _____

Where

What

When

Sketch

Why

How

Specimen 5 _____

Where

What

When

Sketch

Why

How

Specimen 6 _____

Where

What

When

Sketch

Why

How

Specimen 7 _____

Where

What

When

Why

How

Specimen 8 _____

Where

What

When

Why

How

Specimen 9 _____

Where

What

When

Sketch

Why

How

Specimen 10 _____

Where

What

When

Sketch

Why

How

55

Specimen 11 _____

Where ⊹

What 🔍

When 📅

Sketch

Why

How

Specimen 12 _____

Where

What

When

Sketch

Why

How

Specimen 13 _____

Where 🧭

Where

What 🔍

When 📅

Sketch

Why

How

Specimen 14 _____

Where

Where

What

When

Sketch

Why

How

Specimen 15 _____

Where

What

When

Why

How

Specimen 16 _____

Where ✦

What 🔍

When 📅

Sketch

Why

How

Specimen 17 _____

Where

What

When

Why

How

Specimen 18 _____

Where

What

When

Why

How

Specimen 19 _____

Where

What

When

Why

How

Specimen 20 _____

Where

What

When

Sketch

Why

How

Specimen 21 _____

Where 🧭

←_____

←_____

←_____

←_____

What 🔍

←_____

←_____

←_____

←_____

When 📅

←_____

←_____

←_____

←_____

Sketch

Why

How

Specimen 22 _____

Where

What

When

Sketch

Why

How

Specimen 23 _____

Where

What

When

Sketch

Why

How

Specimen 24 _____

Where

What

When

Why

How

Specimen 25 _____

Where

What

When

Sketch

Why

How

Specimen 26 _____

Where

What

When

Why

How

Specimen 27 _____

Where

What

When

Why

How

Specimen 28 _____

Where

What

When

Sketch

Why

How

Specimen 29 _____

Where

What

When

Sketch

Why

How

Specimen 30 _____

Where

What

When

Sketch

Why

How

Specimen 31 _____

Where

What

When

Sketch

Why

How

Specimen 32 _____

Where

What

When

Sketch

Why

How

Specimen 33 _____

Where

What

When

Why

How

Specimen 34 _____

Where

What

When

Sketch

Why

How

Specimen 35 _____

Where

What

When

Why

How

Specimen 36 _____

Where

What

When

Sketch

Why

How

Specimen 37 _____

Where

What

When

Sketch

Why

How

Specimen 38 _____

Where

What

When

Sketch

Why

How

Specimen 39 _____

Where

What

When

Sketch

Why

How

Specimen 40 _____

Where

What

When

Why

How

Specimen 41 _____

Where

What

When

Sketch

Why

How

Specimen 42 _____

Where

What

When

Why

How

Specimen 43 _____

Where

What

When

Sketch

Why

How

Specimen 44 _____

Where

What

When

Sketch

Why

How

Specimen 45 _____

Where

What

When

Sketch

Why

How

Specimen 46 _____

Where

What

When

Sketch

Why

How

Specimen 47 _____

Where

What

When

Why

How

Specimen 48 _____

Where

← _____

← _____

← _____

← _____

What

← _____

← _____

← _____

← _____

← _____

When

← _____

← _____

← _____

← _____

Sketch

Why

How

Specimen 49 _____

Where

What

When

Sketch

Why

How

Specimen 50 _____

Where

What

When

Sketch

Why

How

Harvest
Reference
Pages

Elderberry (Sambucus)

January - February

Page #   Item to be Harvested

_____   _____

_____   _____

_____   _____

_____   _____

_____   _____

_____   _____

_____   _____

_____   _____

_____   _____

_____   _____

_____   _____

_____   _____

_____   _____

_____   _____

_____   _____

_____   _____

_____   _____

_____   _____

_____   _____

March - April

Page #   Item to be Harvested

_____   _____
_____   _____
_____   _____
_____   _____
_____   _____
_____   _____
_____   _____
_____   _____
_____   _____
_____   _____
_____   _____
_____   _____
_____   _____
_____   _____
_____   _____
_____   _____
_____   _____
_____   _____
_____   _____
_____   _____

May - June

Page #   Item to be Harvested

_____   _____

_____   _____

_____   _____

_____   _____

_____   _____

_____   _____

_____   _____

_____   _____

_____   _____

_____   _____

_____   _____

_____   _____

_____   _____

_____   _____

_____   _____

_____   _____

_____   _____

_____   _____

_____   _____

_____   _____

July - August

Page #   Item to be Harvested

_____   _____

_____   _____

_____   _____

_____   _____

_____   _____

_____   _____

_____   _____

_____   _____

_____   _____

_____   _____

_____   _____

_____   _____

_____   _____

_____   _____

_____   _____

_____   _____

_____   _____

_____   _____

_____   _____

September - October

Page #	Item to be Harvested

November - December

Page #	Item to be Harvested

John 3:16-21

1 John 1:9-10

Luke 12:7-12

Romans 3:23-24

1 Peter 1:3-25

Philippians 3:20

Camomile (*Chamaemelum Nobile*)